YOUR
GOLDEN JOURNEY

. . . .

A 45 DAY PILGRIMAGE
TO PERSONAL TRANSFORMATION

JOURNAL

DIANA CHRISTINSON

PEN & PUBLISH
SAINT LOUIS, MISSOURI

Published by Pen & Publish, LLC, USA

www.PenandPublish.com
info@PenandPublish.com

Saint Louis, Missouri
(314) 827-6567

EXCEPTION: "Signs and Symptoms of Inner Peace™"
excerpted from "Symptoms of Inner Peace™"
By Saskia Davis © 1984
For reprint permission contact: symptomsofinnerpeace@gmail.com
http://www.symptomsofinnerpeace.net/Home.html

Book and journal design by Lorna Moy-Masaki.

Mountain path art by Torky at www.Dreamstime.com.

Back cover photo by Stephen Orlick.

Paperback ISBN: 978-1-956897-04-3

1st edition, November 2021

Printed on acid-free paper.

DEDICATION

> Richard,
> I am eternally grateful
> your love continues to
> support my dreams
> and open doors.
> Our time on this planet was short,
> but your presence is forever,
> which is how long
> I will love you.

The true lover
is the one who on
your final day opens
a thousand doors.

— RUMI

An Invitation

 The journey of a thousand miles begins with one step.

—LAO TZU

I invite you to take your first step on an inward journey of self-discovery and awakening. *Your Golden Journey* is a six-week self-study experience filled with meditation, inspiration, and self-reflection. Through daily teachings weaving Eastern philosophy and culture with Western psychology, you will be guided to cultivate more peace, joy, and mindful presence in the moments of your life.

Fill your cup with dedicated sacred time for you. Fifteen minutes of quiet allows you to turn inward and connect with yourself. Read and reflect on practices that will influence how you show up for the precious moments of your day.

YOUR GOLDEN PRACTICE

Sit down in a comfortable seated position—
this could be in a chair or on the floor.

RELAX

With a long spine, relax your shoulders—
soft and down, away from your ears.

CENTERED, AT EASE

Breathe gently through your nose several times.

IN AND OUT
IN AND OUT
IN AND OUT
RELAX

Close your eyes or gaze at a candle.
Slow down your breath.
Let everything go.
Let go of all tension in your body.
And let go of all your thoughts and inner dialogues.
Just sit. Just breathe. Just be.

There is nothing to figure out, no one to impress, nothing to prove.
Experience the joy and peace of meditation.

Enjoy a sacred silence for three to five minutes (or longer—your choice).

Read the Daily Inspiration.
Reflect and Journal.
Incorporate practices into your day.

BONUS:
Visit www.DianaChristinson.com to enjoy a sound-bath
meditation and incorporate it into your Golden Practice.

YOUR GOLDEN JOURNEY

JOURNAL

A SUPPLEMENT TO
YOUR GOLDEN JOURNEY:
A 45-DAY PILGRIMAGE TO
PERSONAL TRANSFORMATION

DAY 1

Locate Yourself

Lost
BY DAVID WAGONER

Stand still. The trees ahead and bushes beside you
Are not lost. Wherever you are is called Here,
And you must treat it as a powerful stranger,
Must ask permission to know it and be known.
The forest breathes. Listen. It answers,
I have made this place around you.
If you leave it, you may come back again, saying Here.
No two trees are the same to Raven.
No two branches are the same to Wren.
If what a tree or a bush does is lost on you,
You are surely lost. Stand still. The forest knows
Where you are. You must let it find you.

Reflection:

Do you remember a time when you stopped to locate yourself? How did you choose to navigate from your true north?

Draw a red dot in your journal. Next to it, write, *I AM HERE*. Map how you navigated through your forests and storms of life to be here, today. Write out parts of your life story, your hero's journey, where you used your internal compass and true north to find your way.

_____

_____

_____

_____
_____
_____
_____
_____
_____
_____
_____
_____
_____
_____
_____
_____
_____
_____
_____
_____
_____
_____
_____
_____
_____
_____
_____
_____
_____
_____
_____

_____

_____

_____

_____

_____

_____

_____

_____

_____

_____

_____

_____

_____

_____

_____

_____

_____

_____

_____

_____

_____

_____

_____

_____

_____

_____

_____

_____

DAY 2

Follow Your Passions

The way to find out about happiness is to keep your mind on those moments when you feel most happy, when you are really happy - not excited, not just thrilled, but deeply happy. This requires a little bit of self-analysis. What is it that makes you happy? Stay with it, no matter what people tell you. This is what is called following your bliss.

— JOSEPH CAMPBELL

Reflection:

Reflect on the passions that brought you to where you are today.

Where do you want to go? What are your dreams, passions, and loves? What do you get excited about? What stirs your soul?

Make a list of two or three things that bring you joy, that ignite your passion.

_____

_____

_____

_____

_____

_____

_____

_____

_____

_____

_____

_____

_____

_____

_____

_____

_____

_____

_____

_____

_____

_____

_____

_____

_____

_____

_____

_____

_____

 DAY 3 _____

Mastering Gratitude

In the end though, maybe we must all give up trying to pay back the people in this world who sustain our lives. In the end, maybe it's wiser to surrender before the miraculous scope of human generosity and to just keep saying 'Thank You' forever and sincerely, for as long as we have voices.

—ELIZABETH GILBERT

Reflection:

Create a gratitude journal and fill the pages with days, weeks, and years of practicing gratitude. Notice how this shifts your daily perspective. Observe how your energy and mental patterns change and happiness increases. After ten thousand hours of practicing Gratitude Meditation, your transformation will inspire you to continue this practice for the rest of your life.

_____

_____

_____

_____

_____

_____

_____

_____

_____

_____

_____

_____

_____

_____

_____

_____

_____

_____

_____

_____

_____

_____

_____

_____

_____

_____

_____

_____

Remember, remember, this is now, and now, and now. Live it, feel it, cling to it. I want to become acutely aware of all I've taken for granted. —SYLVIA PLATH

DAY 4

Breathe with Your Nose, Eat with Your Mouth.

The more you believe in the power of thought,
and the more you listen to your breath, the
greater changes you can create in your life.

—STIG SEVERINSEN

Reflection:

Observe your own breath, as well as other people's breathing.
Do you notice yourself and others breathing through the mouth?

_____

_____

_____

_____

_____

_____

_____

_____

_____

_____

_____

_____

_____

_____

_____

_____

_____

_____

_____

_____

_____

_____

_____

_____

_____

_____

_____

_____

_____

_____

_____

_____

_____

_____

_____

DAY 5 _____

Unplug & Reset

Within you there is a stillness and a sanctuary to which you can retreat at any time and be yourself.

—HERMANN HESSE

Reflection:

Note how much time you spend on your devices.

How could you decrease your device time?

How could you increase your Off time?

_____
_____
_____
_____
_____
_____
_____
_____
_____
_____
_____

DAY 6

Space Training

Everything can be taken from a man but one thing: the last of the human freedoms-

to choose one's attitude in any given set of circumstances, to choose one's own way.

—VIKTOR E. FRANKL

Reflection:

Today, look for opportunities to pause and choose.

At the end of the day, write down any successful pauses.

If you didn't have successful pauses today, take one situation or conversation from the day that could've gone differently. Rewrite it with your own pause and choose scenario to consider a new version of your story.

_____

_____

_____

_____

_____

_____

_____

_____

_____

_____

_____

_____

_____

_____

_____

_____

_____

_____

_____

_____

_____

_____

_____

_____

_____

_____

_____

_____

_____

_____

_____

_____

_____

_____

_____

DAY 7

Catch a Thought and Flip It

We do one thing or another; we stay the same, or we change. Congratulations, if you have changed.

— MARY OLIVER

Reflection:

What patterns are you continually repeating without resolution? Where does your mind go as you move through your day? Notice the messaging in your thoughts and feelings when thinking about different aspects of your life—family, work, health, news... Reflect on how changing the way you respond might change the outcome and create new possibilities. Journal moments throughout your days when you chose to Catch It and Flip It.

_____

_____

_____

_____

_____

_____

_____

_____

_____

_____

_____

_____

_____

_____

_____

_____

_____

_____

_____

_____

_____

_____

_____

_____

_____

_____

_____

_____

_____

_____

_____

_____

_____

_____

_____

DAY 8

Imaginal Cells

I believe that imagination is stronger than knowledge. That myth is more potent than history. That dreams are more powerful than facts. That hope always triumphs over experience. That laughter is the only cure for grief. And I believe that love is stronger than death.

— ROBERT FULGHUM

Reflection:

What are you imagining today? What previews are playing in your mind? Remember, you are the writer. What miracles will you unfold on your Golden Journey?

_____

_____

_____

_____

_____

_____

_____

_____

_____

DAY 9

Travel Light

The question of what you want to own is actually the question of how you want to live your life.

—MARIE KONDO

Reflection:

Notice how you feel after giving away something you had kept for a long time or felt you might need in the future, or something that was expensive. Go through parts of your home and see where you could create more flow.

_____

_____

_____

_____

_____

_____

_____

_____

_____

_____

_____

_____

_____

_____

_____

_____

_____

_____

_____

_____

_____

_____

_____

_____

_____

_____

_____

_____

_____

_____

_____

_____

_____

_____

_____

_____

_____

_____

_____

_____

❋ DAY 10 _____

I Make My Path

If you can see your path laid out in front of you step by step, you know it's not your path. Your own path you make with every step you take. That's why it's your path.

—JOSEPH CAMPBELL

Reflection:

How does your favorite hero movie inspire your life's journey? Identify chapters of your life as comedy, drama, mystery, or unexpected romance.

Look at the bigger story of your life. Map out the chapters of your life history. What twists and turns and unexpected roads brought you to where you are today? How have you made your own path?

_____

_____

_____

_____

_____

_____

_____

_____

_____

☀ DAY 11

Move the Furniture

Life is the constant opportunity to wake up.
— BYRON KATIE

Reflection:

Observe how you feel when you *Move the Furniture*. Notice how your daily patterns of seeing, doing, and being shift.

_____

_____

_____

_____

_____

_____

_____

_____

_____

_____

_____

_____

_____

_____

_____

_____

 DAY 12

Peace Out

"Signs and Symptoms of Inner Peace™"

By Saskia Davis © 1984
Excerpted from SYMPTOMS OF INNER PEACE

*A tendency to think and act spontaneously
rather than on fears based on past experiences*

An unmistakable ability to enjoy each moment

A loss of interest in judging other people

A loss of interest in judging self

A loss of interest in interpreting the actions of others

A loss of interest in conflict

A loss of ability to worry

Frequent, overwhelming episodes of appreciation

*Contented feelings of connectedness
with others & nature*

Frequent attacks of smiling

*An increasing tendency to let things
happen rather than make them happen*

*An increased susceptibility to love extended by others
and the uncontrollable urge to extend it.*

Reflection:

What are *your* symptoms of peace? Singing? Being silly? Sleeping well and waking up with energy? Smiling? Being kind to others and yourself?

Create a personal list of your "Signs and Symptoms of Inner Peace™."

 DAY 13

Artist in You

Do whatever brings you to life. Follow your own fascinations, obsessions and compulsions. Trust them. Create whatever causes a revolution in your heart. The rest will take care of itself.

—ELIZABETH GILBERT

Reflection:

What are the things that you feel express your extraordinary qualities?
    Write them down.
    Refer to yourself as an artist.
    Use your journal as a space to begin adding color and creativity.

_____

_____

_____

_____

_____

_____

_____

_____

_____

_____

_____

_____

_____

_____

_____

_____

_____

_____

_____

_____

_____

_____

_____

_____

_____

_____

_____

_____

_____

_____

_____

_____

_____

_____

_____

_____

DAY 14

I Am the Master

A certain amount of opposition is a great help to a man. Kites rise against, not with, the wind. Even a head wind is better than none. No man ever worked his voyage anywhere in a dead calm.

— JOHN NEAL

Reflection:

What is worth spending your time doing? Do it with full intention, and do it well. While having coffee with a friend, do you look at your phone, take a call, feel rushed, think about what is next on the agenda? Are you talking on the phone while watering the plants? What would it feel like to simply enjoy being outside, hearing the birds, observing growth or the change in seasons reflected in your yard?

_____

_____

_____

_____

_____

_____

_____

_____

_____

_____

_____

_____

_____

_____

_____

_____

_____

_____

_____

_____

_____

_____

_____

_____

_____

_____

_____

_____

_____

_____

When everything seems to be going against you, remember that the airplane takes off against the wind, not with it.

—attributed to HENRY FORD

 DAY 15

Choose Happiness

Happiness is available.
Please help yourself to it.

—THICH NHAT HANH

Reflection:

Observe times you were able to catch yourself going down an unhappy path in your mind. How were you able to choose a happier thought? Did you choose gratitude or step back and get a bigger perspective? Write a few examples. Continue to reflect and journal throughout your weeks.

_____

_____

_____

_____

_____

_____

_____

_____

_____

_____

_____

_____

_____

_____

_____

_____

_____

_____

_____

_____

_____

_____

_____

_____

_____

_____

_____

_____

_____

_____

_____

_____

_____

_____

_____

*Happiness... not another place, in this place,
not another hour, but this hour.*

—WALT WHITMAN

 DAY 16

Energy Banking

Every choice we make, every thought and feeling we have, is an act of power that has biological, environmental, social, personal and global consequences. We are everywhere our thoughts are, and thus our personal responsibility includes our energy contributions.

What choices would we make if we could actually see their energy consequences?

— CAROLYN MYSS

Reflection:

Make a list of the things, people, and situations that drain your energy.

Then make a list of the things, people, and situations that recharge you and fill your energy level.

Replace one energy drain with something or someone that recharges you each day.

_____

_____

_____

_____

_____

_____

_____

_____

_____

_____

_____

_____

_____

_____

_____

_____

_____

_____

_____

_____

_____

_____

_____

_____

_____

_____

_____

_____

_____

_____

_____

_____

_____

_____

_____

_____

_____

_____

_____

_____

_____

_____

_____

_____

_____

_____

_____

_____

_____

_____

_____

_____

_____

_____

_____

DAY 17

Get Up and Move

It is not the number of hours sat that are the problem, but rather the long hours of sitting without a break that cause poor modern health. Equally, standing for many hours without a break can be just as harmful to one's health as sitting.

— DR. JOAN VERIKOS

Reflection:

Observe your activity throughout the day. How much time do you spend in a chair? Brainstorm ideas for how to add more movement in your day.

_____

_____

_____

_____

_____

_____

_____

_____

_____

_____

_____

_____

_____

_____

_____

_____

_____

_____

_____

_____

_____

_____

_____

_____

_____

_____

_____

_____

_____

_____

_____

_____

_____

_____

DAY 18

Give a Smile

There is no need for temples; no need for complicated philosophy. Our own brain, our own heart is our temple; the philosophy is kindness.

—HIS HOLINESS THE 14TH DALAI LAMA

Reflection:

Do you remember the last time a smile made your day? Reflect on moments you remember smiling at someone, perhaps a stranger, and getting a smile back in return. How did it make you feel?

_____

_____

_____

_____

_____

_____

_____

_____

_____

_____

_____

_____

_____

_____

_____

_____

_____

_____

_____

_____

_____

_____

_____

_____

_____

_____

_____

_____

_____

_____

_____

_____

_____

_____

 DAY 19

Nature's Medicine

Live in each season as it passes; breathe air, drink the drink, taste the fruit, and resign yourself to the influences of each.

— HENRY DAVID THOREAU

Your Nature's Medicine Prescription:

- Daily dose of time outside
- Have your morning tea or coffee outside
- Sacred silence and journal under a tree
- Lunch or lunch break walk outside
- Evening walk through your neighborhood
- Weekly long hike in a local park or forest

Reflection:

Reflect on how you feel when you take your dose of *nature's medicine*.

_____

_____

_____

_____

_____

_____

_____

_____

_____

_____

_____

_____

_____

_____

_____

_____

_____

_____

_____

_____

_____

_____

_____

_____

_____

_____

_____

_____

_____

_____

_____

Some men go fishing all their lives without realizing that it is not the fish they are after.
—HENRY DAVID THOREAU

DAY 20

Forest Bathing

There is no medicine you can take that has such a direct influence on your health as a walk in a beautiful forest.

—DR. QING LI

Reflection:

Write in your journal or meditate on how you felt when you spent time in nature, forest bathing with your five senses. Reflect and describe how your senses were awakened through your forest bath.

_____

_____

_____

_____

_____

_____

_____

_____

_____

_____

_____

_____

_____

_____

_____

_____

_____

_____

_____

_____

_____

_____

_____

_____

_____

_____

_____

_____

_____

_____

_____

_____

_____

_____

_____

_____

_____

DAY 21 _____

Barn's Burnt Down

Sometimes with
the bones of the black
sticks left when the fire
has gone out
someone has written
something new
in the ashes
of your life.
You are not leaving.
Even as the light
fades quickly now,
you are arriving.

By David Whyte, from the poem, "The Journey."

Reflection:

Identify parts of your life when you experienced a separation or loss that brought you to a new place that transformed you. Write down losses that granted you opening or perspective.

Use this as a reminder the next time you feel a loss or a change.

_____

_____

_____

_____

_____

_____

_____

_____

_____

_____

_____

_____

_____

_____

_____

_____

_____

_____

_____

_____

_____

_____

_____

_____

_____

_____

_____

_____

_____

_____

DAY 22

Lucky Me!

The best things that have ever happened to me have not been the result of anything I have done. Some might say that is luck. I call them blessings and in some cases miracles.

—TOM KRAUSE

Reflection:

Reflect on five to ten things that you are grateful for. After citing each one individually, recite or write the mantra Lucky Me. Notice how you feel when you add feeling lucky and blessed to your daily gratitude.

_____

_____

_____

_____

_____

_____

_____

_____

_____

_____

DAY 23 _____

Wild Life

Trust yourself, doubt nothing that comes from inspiration, deny nothing that comes from imagination, dismiss nothing that comes from intuition. It is your heart that holds your vision, trust yourself.

— D O R I A N   I S R A E L

Reflection:

What did you do that made today great?

What will you do to make tomorrow great?

Reflect on or write three words—one, wild, and precious. How do these describe your life?

_____

_____

_____

_____

_____

_____

_____

_____

_____

_____

_____

_____

_____

_____

_____

_____

_____

_____

_____

_____

_____

_____

_____

_____

_____

_____

_____

_____

_____

_____

_____

_____

_____

_____

_____

_____

_____

_____

_____

_____

_____

_____

_____

_____

_____

_____

_____

_____

_____

_____

_____

_____

_____

_____

_____

_____

_____

_____

_____

Trust yourself and you will know how to live.

— GOETHE

❋ DAY 24

Giving Bread

We make a living by what we get,
but we make a life by what we give.
— WINSTON CHURCHILL

Reflection:

Journal or sit in reflection and think of one to three special gifts you
have given that brought you deep joy. Remember receiving a gift that
was more than the gift or act itself—one that gave you hope, made
you feel loved, and brought you joy.

_____

_____

_____

_____

_____

_____

_____

_____

_____

_____

_____

_____

Be kind whenever possible. It is always possible.
—HIS HOLINESS THE 14TH DALAI LAMA

DAY 25

A Healthy Mental Diet

The greatest weapon against stress is our ability to choose one thought over another.

— WILLIAM JAMES

Reflection:

At the end of your day, ask yourself: What thoughts did I consume *(or what consumed me)* throughout this day?

Write down what created negative thoughts in your headspace today and where they were created. Perhaps it's a person or situation at work or an aspect of your relationship that makes you impatient or irritable.

Write down any thought patterns or autopilot reactions you recognized.

Pause and reflect, then *choose* a different thought. Write it down.

_____

_____

_____

_____

_____

_____

_____

_____

_____

_____

_____

_____

_____

_____

_____

_____

_____

_____

_____

_____

_____

_____

_____

_____

_____

_____

_____

_____

_____

_____

_____

_____

_____

You find what you look for: good or evil, problems or solutions.

—JOHN M. TEMPLETON

 DAY 26

A Garland of Gratitude

Appreciation can make a day, even change a life. Your willingness to put it into words is all that is necessary.

—MARGARET COUSINS

Reflection:

Open your heart and mind to the many teachers who have shared their light on your path. Reflect and journal on how they have impacted your life.

_____

_____

_____

_____

_____

_____

_____

_____

_____

_____

_____

_____

_____

_____

_____

_____

_____

_____

_____

_____

_____

_____

_____

_____

_____

_____

_____

_____

_____

_____

_____

_____

_____

_____

_____

_____

_____

_____

☀ DAY 27 _____

Bring the Outdoors In

*Plants give us oxygen for the lungs and for
the soul.*

—LINDA SOLEGATO

Reflection:

How do you feel when you bring nature into your inside spaces?
Reflect and journal about how nature's medicine has changed how
you felt or perhaps how you responded to a situation in your day.
Did your indoor forest bath bring you joy? Did it help you slow down
or gain perspective?

_____

_____

_____

_____

_____

_____

_____

_____

_____

_____

_____

_____

_____

❄ DAY 28

Dancing in the Rain

Dare, dream, dance, smile and sing loudly! And have faith that love is an unstoppable force.

—SUZANNE BROCKMANN

Reflection:

Make a play-list of things that brought you joy when you were young. Make a second play-list of activities and things that currently bring you joy. Reflect on what you might bring into your current joy from your past. Journal new ideas to bring joy out of the closet and into your life.

_____

_____

_____

_____

_____

_____

_____

_____

_____

_____

_____

_____

_____

_____

_____

_____

_____

_____

_____

_____

_____

_____

_____

_____

_____

_____

_____

_____

_____

_____

_____

_____

_____

_____

_____

_____

_____

_____

_____

_____

_____

_____

_____

_____

_____

_____

_____

_____

_____

_____

_____

_____

_____

_____

_____

_____

_____

_____

_____

_____

_____

_____

✸ DAY 29 _____

The Invitation

I want to know what sustains you from the inside when all else falls away.

—ORIAH MOUNTAIN DREAMER

Reflection:

Read the poem in its entirety, and handwrite the words in your journal. Underline and highlight the parts most meaningful to you at this time in your life's journey.

Write your own invitation. What questions would you ask? What stirs your soul? What do you dare to dream?

_____

_____

_____

_____

_____

_____

_____

_____

_____

_____

_____

_____

_____

_____

✺ DAY 30

Reach for the Sun

Every great dream begins with a dreamer. Always remember, you have within you the strength, the patience and the passion to reach for the stars to change the world.

—HARRIET TUBMAN

Reflection:

Copy or handwrite the Best Exotic Marigold Hotel quote in your journal or in a place to remind you that the path ahead is yours to create.

What is your sun? What nourishes you?

Make a list.

> *Hikes in nature*
>
> *Watching butterflies*
>
> *Gardening*
>
> *Walking the dogs*

_____

_____

_____

_____

_____

_____

_____

_____

_____

_____

_____

_____

_____

_____

_____

_____

_____

_____

_____

_____

_____

_____

_____

_____

_____

_____

_____

_____

_____

_____

_____

_____

_____

_____

_____

_____

_____

_____

_____

_____

_____

_____

_____

_____

_____

_____

_____

_____

The person who risks nothing, does nothing, has nothing. All we know about the future is that it will be different. But perhaps what we fear is that it will be the same. So we must celebrate the changes. Because, as someone once said, "Everything will be all right in the end. And if it's not all right, then trust me: it's not yet the end."

—THE BEST EXOTIC MARIGOLD HOTEL

❄ DAY 31

Wabi-Sabi

I am a frayed and nibbled survivor in a fallen world, and I am getting along. I am aging and eaten and have done my share of eating too. I am not washed and beautiful, in control of a shining world in which everything fits, but instead am wondering awed about on a splintered wreck I've come to care for, whose gnawed trees breathe a delicate air, whose bloodied and scarred creatures are my dearest companions, and whose beauty bats and shines not in its imperfections but overwhelmingly in spite of them...

—ANNIE DILLARD

Reflection:

Journal and document when you start to observe wabi-sabi in the way you see beauty, think, and live.

_____

_____

_____

_____

✺ DAY 32

Kintsugi

The point of kintsugi is to treat broken pieces and their repair as part of the history of an object. A break is something to remember, something of value, a way to make the piece more beautiful, rather than something to disguise. They use gold, not invisible superglue, because mistakes shouldn't be considered ugly. Broken pieces and their repair merely contribute to the story of an object, they don't ruin it.

— PENNY REID

Reflection:

Reflect on and journal your history. Open your heart and mind to review your unique life story and where your spirit became scarred or cracked. Journal how these cracks have made you who you are today.

_____

_____

_____

_____

_____

_____

_____

_____

_____

_____

_____

_____

_____

_____

_____

_____

_____

_____

_____

_____

_____

_____

_____

_____

_____

_____

_____

_____

_____

Some people see scars, and it is wounding they remember. To me they are proof of the fact that there is healing.

—LINDA HOGAN

☀ DAY 33

Plant a Garden

So plant your own gardens and decorate your own soul, instead of waiting for someone to bring you flowers.

—JORGE LUIS BORGES

Reflection:

Reflect and journal about times you have grown a fruit, vegetable, or flowering plant. It might be a memory from your childhood or perhaps a more recent experience. Was it exciting and joyful to water a plant and watch it grow? Was it therapeutic to weed and care for the plant?

_____

_____

_____

_____

_____

_____

_____

_____

_____

_____

_____

_____
_____
_____
_____
_____
_____
_____
_____
_____
_____
_____
_____
_____
_____
_____
_____
_____
_____
_____
_____
_____
_____
_____
_____
_____

DAY 34

If Not Now, WHEN?

The butterfly counts not months but moments, and has time enough.

—RABINDRANATH TAGORE

Reflection:

What are your "yes, buts"? Reflect and journal about what stops you from choosing how you spend the moments of your day.

What is something you have been dreaming or feel passionate about doing? As you reflect on your passions, pay attention to how it makes you feel to give this dream attention. Open the door to possibility by considering how you might begin a new dream.

_____

_____

_____

_____

_____

_____

_____

_____

_____

_____

_____

_____

_____

_____

_____

_____

_____

_____

_____

_____

_____

_____

_____

_____

_____

_____

_____

_____

_____

_____

_____

_____

_____

_____

_____

_____

_____

_____

❋DAY 35 _____

Lose Your Shoes

*Walk, stand or sit barefoot on the ground...
At the end of your time you will feel better.
As you feel better, a light bulb will go off in
your head. You will realize that although
you live on the surface of the earth, your
lifestyle has separated you from the
limitless healing energy that, unknown to
you, the surface beneath your feet holds.
It's there, and always there, and yours for
the taking.*

   —CLINTON OBER, STEPHEN T. SINATRA, M.D.,
     MARTIN ZUCKER

Reflection:

Reflect on the last time you walked barefoot or sat in the grass, sand, dirt. How did it make you feel? How did it affect your mood or your sleep? Write about your experience.

_____

_____

_____

_____

_____

_____

_____

_____

_____

_____

_____

_____

_____

_____

_____

_____

_____

_____

_____

_____

_____

_____

_____

_____

_____

_____

_____

_____

_____

❄ DAY 36 _____

The Invisible Gift

Remember that wherever your heart is,
there you will find your treasure.

— PAULO COELHO

Reflection:

Reflect and journal about who you love. If you knew you were going to say a last goodbye, what invisible gift would you give them? How would you treat them? What would you say?

_____

_____

_____

_____

_____

_____

_____

_____

_____

_____

_____

_____

_____

DAY 37

How We Spend Today

I cannot cause light, the most I can do is put myself in the path of it's beam.

—ANNIE DILLARD

Reflection:

How do you want to spend your day today? What is stopping you from doing it?

List three ways to skip and move joyfully through the day. List three ways you drag yourself through the day.

_____

_____

_____

_____

_____

_____

_____

_____

_____

_____

_____

_____

_____

☀ DAY 38 _____

What If?

In oneself lies the world, and if you know how to look and learn, the door is there and the key is in your hand.

— K R I S H N A M U T R I

Reflection:

Reflect on your life story and make a list of impossible things you imagined and brought into being. Now create a new list. What will you imagine for today and tomorrow?

_____

_____

_____

_____

_____

_____

_____

_____

_____

_____

_____

_____

_____

 DAY 39

Awaken From Your Sensory Slumber

I am restored in beauty, I am restored in beauty, I am restored in beauty.

— NAVAJO PRAYER

Reflection:

What are you noticing and grateful for today? Nature's abundant gifts surround you.

How can you wake up to the beauty around you and let it inspire you?

_____

_____

_____

_____

_____

_____

_____

_____

_____

_____

_____

_____

❄ DAY 40 _____

The We of Me

Relationships are essentially spiritual messengers. They bring into our lives - and we into theirs - revelations about our strengths and weaknesses.

— CAROLINE MYSS, PH.D.

Reflection:

Reflect and journal about your earliest memories of your We. Who are the people—family, friends, teachers—who have influenced who you are today? Write a list of your friends from elementary school, high school, college, or your first job. How are they part of your Me? Make a list of the friends and family who surround you today—they are your mirror.

_____

_____

_____

_____

_____

_____

_____

_____

_____

_____

_____

_____

_____

_____

_____

_____

_____

_____

_____

_____

_____

_____

_____

_____

_____

_____

_____

_____

_____

_____

_____

_____

_____

_____

_____

_____

_____

_____

_____

_____

_____

_____

_____

_____

_____

_____

_____

_____

_____

_____

_____

_____

_____

_____

_____

_____

What we have enjoyed, we can never lose...
All that we love deeply becomes a part of us.
—HELEN KELLER

✳ DAY 41 _____

A Message From a Wasp

You suppose that you are the lock on the door, but you are the key that opens it.

— R U M I

Reflection:

Reflect on times you have felt like the wasp banging your head against an open door.

    Reflect and journal about the moments when you used one of your practices to change a negative loop.

_____

_____

_____

_____

_____

_____

_____

_____

_____

_____

_____

_____

_____

_____

_____

_____

_____

_____

_____

_____

_____

_____

_____

_____

_____

_____

_____

_____

_____

_____

_____

_____

_____

_____

_____

_____

_____

_____

_____

_____

_____

_____

_____

_____

_____

_____

_____

_____

_____

_____

_____

_____

_____

_____

_____

_____

_____

_____

_____

_____

_____

_____

_____

_____

_____

*The handle is on the inside of the door;
only we can open it.*

—JOHN O'DONOHUE

DAY 42

Influencers

We are the ones we have been waiting for.

—ALICE WALKER

Reflection:

Think of your actions as a way of being. How are they influencing others? List the ways you would like your actions, words, and life to affect others.

_____

_____

_____

_____

_____

_____

_____

_____

_____

_____

_____

_____

_____

_____

_____

_____

_____

_____

_____

_____

_____

_____

_____

_____

_____

_____

_____

_____

_____

_____

_____

_____

_____

_____

_____

_____

_____

 DAY 43

Happiness is an Inside Job

The way to find out about happiness is to keep your mind on those moments when you feel most happy, when you are really happy- not excited, not just thrilled, but deeply happy. This requires a little bit of self-analysis. What is it that makes you happy? Stay with it, no matter what people tell you.

— JOSEPH CAMPBELL

Reflection:

Calculate your waking hours, which likely take up between sixteen and eighteen hours of each day. How many hours out of the day would you like to be happy? Define your happiness. What does it look and feel like to you? Create a list of happy feelings and situations.

_____

_____

_____

_____

_____

_____

_____

_____

_____

_____

_____

_____

_____

_____

_____

_____

_____

_____

_____

_____

_____

_____

_____

_____

_____

_____

_____

_____

_____

_____

_____

_____

_____

_____

_____

_____

_____

_____

_____

_____

_____

_____

_____

_____

_____

_____

_____

_____

_____

_____

_____

_____

_____

_____

_____

_____

_____

_____

_____

While we may not be able to control all that happens to us, we can control what happens inside us.

—BENJAMIN FRANKLIN

✸ DAY 44

Love and Happiness

I just want to live everyday as if I have deliberately come back to this one day, to enjoy it as if it was the full, final day of my extraordinary ordinary life.

Everyday all we can do is our best to relish this remarkable ride.

FROM THE MOVIE, *ABOUT TIME*

Reflection:

What would you write on the back of a dollar to remind you of your true wealth, the most important gifts? What would fill your list? How will you define true wealth?

_____

_____

_____

_____

_____

_____

_____

_____

_____

❀ DAY 45

You Are the Hero

For all that has been, thank you!
For all that is to come, yes!

—DAG HAMMARSKJÖLD

Reflection:

What are your superpowers, your strength, skills, personal assets?
How do you use them in being the hero or heroine of your life
adventure? How can you remind yourself of your skills and gifts in
the moments of your day?

_____

_____

_____

_____

_____

_____

_____

_____

_____

_____

_____

_____

_____

_____

_____

_____

_____

_____

_____

_____

_____

_____

_____

_____

_____

_____

_____

_____

_____

_____

_____

_____

_____

_____

_____

_____

_____

_____

_____

May this six-week journey continue to remind you that you are the hero or heroine, star and writer, of your life story. I also hope that this special time of reflection and inspiration will continue to remind you that your life is your journey, your great adventure, and that you direct your path.

I invite you to continue starting your day with your Golden Practice and devoting sacred time to yourself. Revisit the journey when you are ready for more growth and change. Share the journey with a friend, partner, or family member, and commit to the journey together. You can use Your Golden Journey for daily or weekly inspiration. Let it remind you of your golden potential on your path of life.

Blessings on your life journey.

DAY 46

The Journey Continues...

We are the Ones We've Been Waiting For

*You have been telling people that this is the Eleventh Hour,
now you must go back and tell the people that this is the Hour.
And there are things to be considered...*

*Where are you living?
What are you doing?
What are your relationships?
Are you in right relation?
Where is your water?
Know your garden.
It is time to speak your truth.
Create your community.
Be good to each other.*

And do not look outside yourself for your leader.

*Then he clasped his hands together, smiled, and said,
"This could be a good time! There is a river flowing now very fast.
t is so great and swift that there are those who will be afraid.
They will try to hold on to the shore. They will feel they are being torn
apart and will suffer greatly. Know the river has its destination.
The elders say we must let go of the shore, push off into the middle
of the river, keep our eyes open, and our heads above the water.*

*And I say, see who is in there with you and celebrate.
At this time in history, we are to take nothing personally, least of all
ourselves. For the moment that we do, our spiritual growth and journey
come to a halt. The time of the lone wolf is over. Gather yourselves!
Banish the word 'struggle' from your attitude and your vocabulary.
All that we do now must be done in a sacred manner and in celebration.
We are the ones we've been waiting for.*

—Hopi Elders' Prophecy, June 8, 2000

Reflection:

On your continued Golden Journey, find the pause, touch your heart,
listen to your innermost wisdom. YOU are the one you've been
waiting for.

_____

_____

_____

_____

_____

_____

_____

_____

_____

_____

_____

_____

_____

_____

_____

_____

_____

_____

_____

_____

_____

_____

_____

_____

_____

_____

_____

_____

_____

_____

_____

_____

_____

_____

_____

_____

_____

_____

_____

_____

_____

_____